THE WORLD IS FULL OF THINGS
WE NEVER SEE...

ALCHEMY

ALCHEMY WAS POPULAR IN EUROPE IN ANCIENT TIMES, AND IN THE MIDDLE AGES. IT WAS A MIX OF MAGIC AND SCIENCE. LATER, SCIENCE AND MAGIC BROKE APART, SO NOW, IN SCHOOL, THEY TEACH YOU CHEMISTRY, NOT ALCHEMY.

ALCHEMY AND MAGIC ARE TAUGHT ONLY AT MAGIC SCHOOLS, LIKE THE ONE WHERE I WORK, THE NORTH LANDING ACADEMY OF MAGIC ARTS. BECAUSE MANY SCIENCES, SUCH AS CHEMISTRY, PHYSICS, AND MEDICINE TOOK A LOT FROM ALCHEMY, ALCHEMISTS CALL THEIR ART *THE MOTHER OF ALL SCIENCE AND WISDOM*. ONE OF THE GREAT SKILLS ALCHEMISTS DEVELOPED WAS THE ART OF MAKING POTIONS AND ELIXIRS. MANY MEDICINES IN ANCIENT DAYS WERE ALCHEMICAL POTIONS.

ALCHEMICAL POTIONS ARE OFTEN USED IN SPELLS, ESPECIALLY IN PROTECTION SPELLS TO KEEP YOU SAFE FROM DRAGONS. YOU THINK: BUT THERE ARE NO DRAGONS AROUND! MANY PEOPLE THINK DRAGONS ARE FAIRY-TALE CREATURES, BUT WHEN YOU START LEARNING MAGIC, YOU BEGIN NOTICING THINGS THAT OTHERS DON'T SEE. ...AND THOSE THINGS BEGIN NOTICING YOU.

Dragon Spell 1

This page is partially lost. It seems to tell the story of a battle with a dragon that didn't end well. The spell is the classic Keep Dragons Away protection spell.

...him
...orever
...its tail.

...his last words.

...my dragon away.

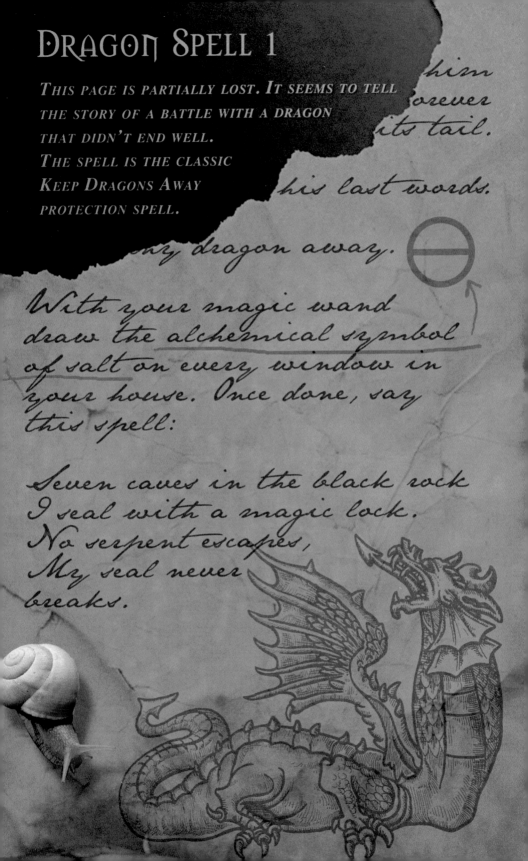

With your magic wand draw the alchemical symbol of salt on every window in your house. Once done, say this spell:

Seven caves in the black rock
I seal with a magic lock.
No serpent escapes,
My seal never breaks.

THE EMERALD TABLET

THE IDEAS OF ALCHEMY COME FROM THE FAMOUS
EMERALD TABLET OF HERMES TRISMEGISTUS.
TRISMEGISTUS = *THREE TIMES THE GREATEST* IN GREEK.
WHO WAS HERMES TRISMEGISTUS? NOBODY KNOWS.
LEGENDS SAY THIS ANCIENT TABLET
(WHICH NOBODY EVER SAW!) WAS CREATED FROM
ALCHEMICALLY-MADE EMERALD AND HAD THESE WORDS ON IT:

EMERALD

IT IS TRUE THAT WHATEVER IS BELOW
IS LIKE THAT WHICH IS ABOVE;
AND THAT WHICH IS ABOVE
IS LIKE THAT WHICH IS BELOW...
ALL THINGS COME FROM ONE SOURCE,
BY THE WILL AND BY THE WORD
OF THE ONLY ONE
WHO CREATED IT IN HIS MIND...

SO ALCHEMISTS BELIEVED THAT
THE ENERGY COMING FROM THE MIND
OF GOD BECOMES THE MATERIAL
WORLD AND THEN RETURNS BACK
TO ITS SOURCE AS SPIRITUAL ENERGY.
THE ALCHEMICAL SYMBOL OF THIS
IS THE OUROBORUS,
THE SERPENT EATING
ITS OWN TAIL.

FROM A 17TH CENTURY
ALCHEMY BOOK:
HERMES TRISMEGISTUS
WITH THE WORD THEOS
("GOD" IN GREEK)
IN THE SKY.

MATERIAL WORLD = THE WORLD YOU CAN SEE OR TOUCH
SPIRITUAL WORLD = IDEAS, THOUGHTS, SOULS AND MYSTERIES

THE PRINCIPLES OF ALCHEMY

THE 2 MAIN PRINCIPLES OF ALCHEMY ARE:

1. ALL IS FROM ONE

(ALL MATTER AND SPIRIT COME FROM ONE SOURCE)

2. THE WORLD IS MADE OF OPPOSITES

(HOT-COLD, MATTER-SPIRIT, MAN-WOMAN...)

THE ALCHEMIST'S RULE IS:

ORA ET LABORA

= *PRAY AND WORK* IN LATIN,

OR-RAH ET LAB-*BOR*-RAH.

THE WORD *LABORATORY* COMES FROM THIS SAYING.

SINCE ALCHEMISTS BELIEVED THAT *ALL IS FROM ONE*,
THEY THOUGHT THAT YOU CAN TWEAK ANY SUBSTANCE
TO TURN IT INTO ANY OTHER SUBSTANCE, LIKE FOR EXAMPLE
TURN ANY METAL INTO GOLD. THEY WERE TRYING TO BREAK
SUBSTANCES INTO SEPARATE ELEMENTS, MAKE THOSE
ELEMENTS PURE, AND BRING THEM TOGETHER AGAIN,
HOPING TO MAKE GOLD, OR *THE PHILOSOPHER'S STONE*
(SEE *THE PHILOSOPHER'S STONE* CHAPTER).
AS WE KNOW, ALCHEMY NEVER SUCCEEDED IN MAKING
THE PHILOSOPHER'S STONE, BUT IT DID SUCCEED
IN MAKING POWERFUL POTIONS.

THE 3-STEP ALCHEMICAL METHOD:

1. SEPARATION: EXTRACT SUBSTANCES FROM NATURE.

2. PURIFICATION: MAKE THEM PURE.

3. RECOMBINATION: MIX THEM AGAIN.

TO TURN AN ALCHEMICAL POTION INTO A MAGIC POTION YOU
NEED A SPELL. WE WILL COMBINE ALCHEMY AND MAGIC
USING THE ANCIENT SPELLS OF THE NORTH LANDING VAULTS

Collecting Rainwater

FOR OUR ALCHEMICAL POTIONS
WE'LL NEED **RAINWATER**.
ALCHEMISTS BELIEVE THAT
PURE RAINWATER CONTAINS
THE **UNIVERSAL FLAME OF LIFE.**
THIS WILL BE THE FIRST STEP
OF OUR ALCHEMICAL PROCESS: SEPARATION, OR EXTRACTION.
THE ALCHEMICAL SYMBOL FOR WATER IS SHOWN ABOVE.

RAINWATER USED FOR ALCHEMY SHOULD NEVER TOUCH
ANY METAL. SO WE NEVER USE METAL CONTAINERS,
NEVER COLLECT IT FROM A METAL WATER SPOUT,
NOR FROM A ROOF, AND WE MUST CATCH IT BEFORE
IT TOUCHES THE GROUND, OR PLANTS. RAINWATER COLLECTED
AT NIGHT AND PURIFIED IS CALLED *CONDENSED STAR LIGHT.*
RAINWATER COLLECTED DURING
THE DAYTIME AND PURIFIED
IS CALLED THE *SUN POTION.*

YOU CAN JUST LEAVE A GLASS OR PLASTIC CONTAINER
OUTSIDE AND LET IT COLLECT SOME RAINWATER.
IF IT'S WINTER, YOU CAN COLLECT
THE SNOW. IF THE SNOW IS ALREADY LYING ON
THE GROUND, COLLECT THE FRESH TOP LAYER.

DON'T BE SURPRISED IF YOU NOTICE
DUST OR DIRT IN YOUR RAINWATER.
THERE IS A LOT OF DUST IN THE AIR,
AND THERE IS ALSO SMOKE POLLUTION
COMING FROM FACTORIES AND CARS.

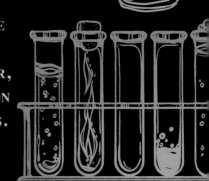

Filtering Rainwater

THE SECOND STEP IN OUR ALCHEMICAL
PROCESS IS PURIFICATION.
FIRST WE FILTER OUR RAINWATER.
YOU CAN USE CLEAN FABRIC, OR
A PAPER NAPKIN, A PAPER TOWEL
OR A COFFEE FILTER. HERE IS HOW:

AFTER THIS FIRST PURIFICATION STEP, COVER
THE CONTAINER WITH FABRIC OR PAPER TO KEEP
DUST OUT, BUT DON'T SEAL IT. YOUR RAINWATER
SHOULD BREATHE. KEEP IT IN A DARK PLACE, AND
NEVER TOUCH THIS WATER WITH YOUR HAND
OR WITH ANY METAL OBJECT.

NEXT COMES DISTILLATION TO MAKE
THE SUN POTION OR CONDENSED STAR LIGHT.

Solar Distillation

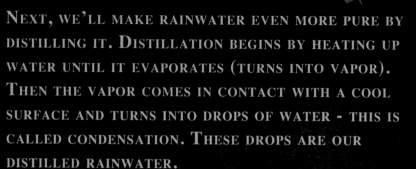

Next, we'll make rainwater even more pure by distilling it. Distillation begins by heating up water until it evaporates (turns into vapor). Then the vapor comes in contact with a cool surface and turns into drops of water - this is called condensation. These drops are our distilled rainwater.

To heat up the water we'll use the energy of the Sun, so wait for a sunny day. This alchemical process is called solar distillation. In Alchemy the Sun is the source of magical transformation. The alchemical symbol of the Sun is the same as the symbol for gold.

Pour some rainwater into a small jar. Put this jar it into a larger jar. Seal the larger jar, draw the sun symbol on the lid or on the side of the jar, and place it in a sunny spot - indoors or outdoors. The rain water will warmup up, evaporate, and appear as drops on the walls of the large jar. It will run down the sides to the bottom. Once there is enough distilled water at the bottom, remove the small jar carefully and pour the distilled rainwater into a special container.

VAPOR DRAGON

ALCHEMISTS WERE PRACTICING MAGIC IN THE DAYS WHEN
MANY PEOPLE BELIEVED THAT ALL MAGIC WAS EVIL
WITCHCRAFT, SO ALCHEMISTS CAME UP WITH SECRET
WAYS TO DESCRIBE THEIR ALCHEMICAL EXPERIMENTS.
THEIR BOOKS ARE MYSTERIOUS AND HARD TO UNDERSTAND.

SOMETIMES, WHEN ALCHEMICAL BOOKS TALK ABOUT
A DRAGON RISING AND OPENING ITS WINGS, IT'S THE PROCESS
OF VAPORISATION.
ANY SUBSTANCE CAN
BE SOLID (LIKE ICE).
IF YOU HEAT IT UP,
IT BECOMES LIQUID (LIKE WATER),
AND IF YOU HEAT IT UP SOME MORE,
IT WILL BE FLYING IN THE AIR
(LIKE VAPOR).
ALCHEMISTS CALLED VAPOR
RISING UP AND SWIRLING
OVER THE HEATED LIQUID
A *DRAGON*.
WHEN THEY TALK ABOUT
KILLING THE DRAGON, IT'S COOLING LIQUIDS TO STOP
VAPORISATION. *DRAGON'S BLOOD* IS CONDENSED LIQUID, LIKE
THE DROPS OF DISTILLED WATER IN OUR DISTILLATION PROCESS.

HEAT ATTRACTS DRAGONS. THAT'S WHY, WORKING ON
POTIONS FOR USE IN DRAGON SPELLS, WE NEVER USE FIRE.
IT'S HARD TO MAKE A LOT OF DISTILLED WATER WITH
SOLAR DISTILLATION, BUT EVEN A FEW DROPS IS ENOUGH.
BE RESPONSIBLE DOING MAGIC, KEEP YOUR FAMILY SAFE
FROM DRAGONS!

Floods at North Landing

One year, as I was teaching the course on Alchemy at the North Landing Academy of Magic Arts, I went down into the underground vaults of the Academy to collect snake eggs for my class. I noticed that the vaults were flooded worse than ever. The flooding happens there every month during the full moon, when the tide rises and the ocean waves crash harder and harder against the underwater walls of the North Landing castle. And also that's when dozens of dragons come from everywhere and land on the cliffs over the towers. You'd better stay indoors during the full moon if you want to graduate one day!

Dr. Martin Burke who taught the History of Magic Arts at the Academy told me he was concerned about the ancient spell books locked in the secret library chamber in the vaults.

THE KEY

AT THAT MOMENT I KNEW
THERE WAS A CONNECTION
BETWEEN THE FLOODING,
THE DRAGONS, AND
THE SPELL BOOKS.
SOME DRAGONS WERE HUGE
AND COULD EASILY BREAK
INTO THE CASTLE. THERE
WAS SOMETHING IN THOSE
SPELL BOOKS THAT
PROTECTED US FROM THE
DRAGON INVASION, AND
THE DRAGONS KNEW THIS
AND WERE WAITING
FOR THE SPELL BOOKS
TO BE DESTROYED.

IT TOOK DR. BURKE
3 MONTHS TO CONVINCE
THE NORTH LANDING ACADEMY
BOARD OF DIRECTORS TO GIVE
HIM THE KEY TO THE SECRET
LIBRARY CHAMBER, AND
EVERY MONTH AT FULL MOON
I THOUGHT THE END WAS NEAR.

WHAT REALLY CONVINCED THEM WAS THAT
THE DRAGONS WERE COMING CLOSER AND CLOSER
TO THE ACADEMY TOWERS. THEY FINALLY
STARTED LANDING ON THE WALLS AND
PEEKING INTO THE CLASSROOM WINDOWS!

In The Vaults

Once we had the key, we made our way underground, wading in the water to get into the chamber. Sure enough, most books were lost forever, torn into pages by snakes that slithered into the library with the flood waters. Many pages were sucked into the ocean through the cracks in the stone floor.

THE SEVEN PAGES

DRAGONS COME IN MANY SHAPES AND FORMS. IF YOU
PRACTICE MAGIC, THEY FEEL IT FROM FAR AWAY AND
SOONER OR LATER THEY COME FOR YOU.

BACK AT MY ALCHEMY LAB, DR.BURKE AND I CLEANED
AND DRIED SEVEN PAGES - ALL THAT WAS LEFT -
OF THE ANCIENT DRAGON SPELL BOOK. THOSE WERE
THE PAGES THAT HAD KEPT US SAFE FROM THE HUNGRY
WINGED BEASTS FOR ALL
THOSE YEARS.

ON THAT DAY
I MADE A PROMISE
TO SHARE
THOSE SPELLS
WITH YOU.

Dragon Spell 2

This page was damaged by fire.
It could be that one of the evil fire-
breathing beasts tried to get hold of it.

The *Water Serpent Spell* is usually cast if you
notice signs of dragon presence in a river or a pond
near your house, or during rain. Maybe you heard
scary howling sounds at night, or the pond water
bubbled, or maybe there is a fog that swirls
into strange shapes, or you have a feeling during
the rain that someone is looking at you through
the window. Cast this spell immediately!

To make the *Meteorite Dust elixir*,
use the Sun Potion or Condensed
Star Light to start. Making this elixir
is the third step of our alchemical
process - recombination.
Pour distilled rainwater into a small
jar, and mix it with filtered rainwater.
Next, find an object made of iron or steel (steel
contains a lot of iron). It can be a nail, a screw,
a key, a spoon, knife, or fork (except silver).
Keep it in the rainwater mix for at least
an hour, and the elixir is ready.
If a metal object sticks to a magnet,
or has rust on it, it's either iron or steel.
Remember these alchemical symbols:

steel

iron

Water
Serpent Spell

Pour the Meteorite Dust
elixir on the ground,
spin yourself 3 times to
the right, and say this spell:

Find the serpent in its lair,
Bind it, chain it,
        keep it there,
If it's out and free to fly,
Rain the daggers
    from the sky.

DAGGERS FROM HEAVEN

METEORS ARE PIECES OF COMETS THAT TRAVEL THROUGH SPACE. MOST METEORS BURN AND DISAPPEAR WHEN THEY HIT THE EARTH'S ATMOSPHERE, BUT SOME REACH THE EARTH. THESE ARE CALLED *METEORITES*. METEORITES ARE ROCKS. 1 IN 10 METEORITES IS MADE OF IRON.

FROM EARTH, METEORS LOOK LIKE SHOOTING STARS. A FEW TIMES A YEAR, COMETS PASS NEAR THE EARTH AND A LOT OF ROCKS FROM THE COMET TAILS ENTER OUR ATMOSPHERE AND BURN. THESE ARE CALLED *METEOR SHOWERS*. SOME ANCIENT PEOPLE CALLED THEM *DAGGERS FROM HEAVEN*. BEFORE THEY KNEW HOW TO MINE IRON, PEOPLE WERE FINDING IRON METEORITES AND MAKING DAGGERS, JEWELRY, AND GIFTS FROM THAT IRON. SCIENTISTS THINK THAT THIS DAGGER FROM THE TOMB OF THE ANCIENT EGYPTIAN KING TUT IS MADE FROM METEORITE IRON. 3300 YEARS AFTER KING TUT'S DEATH, THIS DAGGER HASN'T RUSTED. ITS HANDLE IS MADE FROM GOLD AND ROCK CRYSTAL. IN THE DAYS OF KING TUT IRON WAS MORE EXPENSIVE THAN GOLD.

Colonne ardant. Eſtoille volant.   Comette couee.   Eſtoilles erratiques.

Les trops dernieres ſont eſtoille barbue eſtoille cheuelue z eſtoille couee.

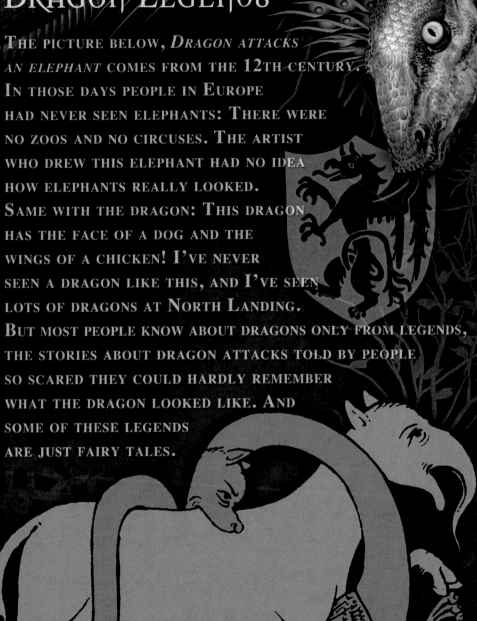

Dragon Legends

The picture below, *Dragon attacks an elephant* comes from the 12th century. In those days people in Europe had never seen elephants: There were no zoos and no circuses. The artist who drew this elephant had no idea how elephants really looked. Same with the dragon: This dragon has the face of a dog and the wings of a chicken! I've never seen a dragon like this, and I've seen lots of dragons at North Landing. But most people know about dragons only from legends, the stories about dragon attacks told by people so scared they could hardly remember what the dragon looked like. And some of these legends are just fairy tales.

The Basilisk

The Basilisk is a monster from the legends of ancient Europe. The word *basilisk* comes from the Greek word *basilikos* which means *little king*. They said basilisks killed their prey with their deadly stare. In the Middle Ages people carried a mirror in their pocket to protect them in case of a basilisk attack. They believed the basilisk would be killed by the stare of its own reflection. Another name for a basilisk is Cockatrice. Legends say a basilisk is born from an egg laid by a rooster and hatched by a toad. Artists drew the basilisk as half-rooster and half-dragon (See picturues below). Are basilisks real? NO. Roosters don't lay eggs!

REAL DRAGONS

IN DIFFERENT PARTS OF THE WORLD THERE ARE DIFFERENT KINDS OF DRAGONS. THE MOST DANGEROUS DRAGONS LIVE IN NORTHERN EUROPE AND NORTH AMERICA. THESE ARE HUGE, SCALY, WINGED, FIRE-BREATHING BEASTS WITH LOTS OF TEETH. SOME OF THEM ARE MAGICAL CREATURES WHO ARE INVISIBLE TO AN UNTRAINED EYE. HERE IS A PICTURE OF **TATZLWURM** FROM AN OLD **GERMAN** BOOK. IT LOOKS LIKE A REAL DRAGON, EXCEPT THE WINGS WOULD HAVE TO BE **10** TIMES BIGGER TO LIFT THIS CREATURE.

IS IT TRUE THAT DRAGONS LIVE IN CAVES AND GUARD THE TREASURES THEY HAVE STOLEN? YES.

THE WORD *DRAGON* COMES FROM **LATIN** *DRACO.* THE MEANING OF THIS WORD IN ANCIENT **ROME** WAS *A HUGE SNAKE.* SOME DRAGONS ARE SERPENTS WITH WINGS LIKE THIS **LINDWURM.** *WURM* OR *WORM* MEANT *SNAKE* OR *DRAGON* IN ANCIENT LANGUAGES OF NORTHER

St. George and the Dragon

St. is short for *Saint*. A *saint* is a hero of the Christian Church. Most saints have sacrificed a lot to help other people. *To sacrifice* means to give up something that is important to you. Some Christian saints sacrificed their life, including St. George.

St. George was a soldier in ancient Rome, in the 3rd century A.D. Roman Emperor Diocletian hated Christians, and sent an order to his army to kill them. St. George was from a Christian family. He tore up the order and left the army. The Emperor was furious, and demanded that St. George come back and give up his Christian faith. St. George refused and was killed.

Then, in the 13th century someone wrote a book telling the story of St. George and a dragon. The dragon was not happy with the 2 sheep a day the people in the town of Silene were feeding it. It wanted to eat kids! The king sent his daughter, the Princess, to be eaten by the dragon, but St. George happened to be

CRITICAL THINKING

SO ALL THOSE SOUNDS AT NIGHT ARE JUST A RAINSTORM, AND MONSTERS UNDER YOUR BED ARE JUST YOUR IMAGINATION. OK. WHAT ABOUT THESE PICTURES OF DESTRUCTION? NOTHING TO DO WITH DRAGONS? *OH NO,* THE GROWNUPS TELL YOU, *IT'S A HURRICANE OR A TORNADO.* HMMM... REALLY? NOTHING TO DO WITH

DRAGONS AT ALL? HOW ABOUT ALL THOSE KNIGHTS KILLING DRAGONS, AND THERE IS NOT A SINGLE STORY ABOUT A KNIGHT LOSING A BATTLE WITH A DRAGON...? MAYBE THAT'S BECAUSE NOBODY SURVIVED TO TELL THOSE STORIES! SEE WHAT I AM GETTING AT? THIS IS CALLED **CRITICAL THINKING.** IT'S WHEN YOU DIG DEEPER LOOKING FOR THE TRUTH. SOME OF THOSE FAIRY-TALE STORIES ARE A LITTLE TOO GOOD TO BE TRUE!

Dragon Spell 3

This page has a strange mark on it looking like a dragon claw scratch. There are dried splotches of some dark red stuff.

Some old *draconology* (science about dragons) books say the claws of the *Night Shade* dragons are gold. That's why this spell is called Gold to Ash, and the elixir we use in it is *Dragon's Claw*.

You cast this spell if you notice some mess outside your house. Does it look like someone was digging in the yard, or tree branches are broken, or the grass is crushed? All these are signs of Night Shade dragons haunting your area.

The alchemical symbols above are for gold and ash. Learn to draw them in the air with your wand. The Dragon Claw elixir attracts dragons who love gold and treasures, so be very careful, and watch your back!

Drop a shiny object into a glass of water. It can be a piece of jewelry, a key, a sparkly bead, or a new coin. Wave your wand over it 3 times saying:
Night Shade Dragon, are you near?
Make your presence known and clear.

Gold to Ash Spell

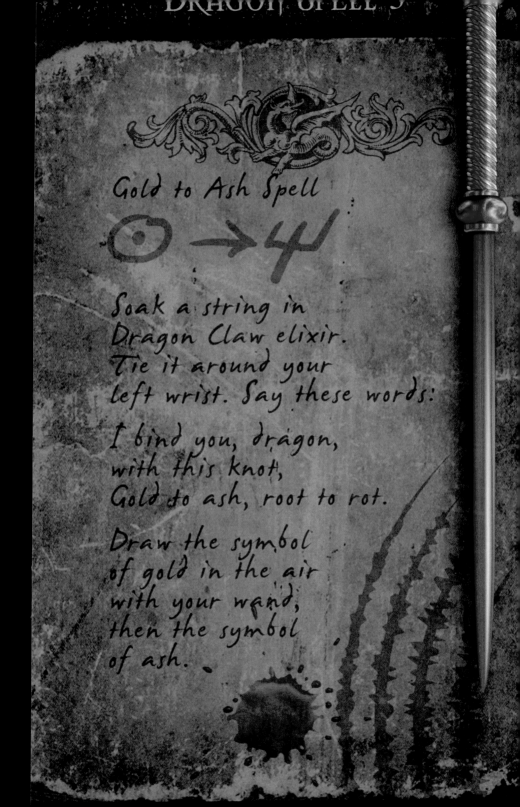

Soak a string in
Dragon Claw elixir.
Tie it around your
left wrist. Say these words:

I bind you, dragon,
with this knot,
Gold to ash, root to rot.

Draw the symbol
of gold in the air
with your wand,
then the symbol
of ash.

CAVES

Dragons live and hoard their treasures in caves. Caves are tunnels cut in rock by ancient rivers. Most caves have a river running through them, and

the water is always dripping from the cave ceiling. As it drips, it carries with it rock dust. Over thousands of years this dripping forms *STALACTITES*, rocks that hang down from the ceiling and *STALAGMITES*, rocks rising from the floor. Stalactites and stalagmites grow and grow, and often meet, making weird columns. Ancient people lived in caves too. Caves protected them from storms and wild animals. Here is a picture of Petra, a cave city from the 4th century B.C. in the country of Jordan. And this is a cave Christian

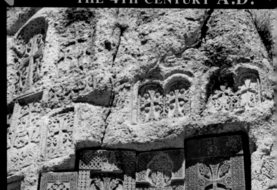

monastery in Armenia built in the 4th century A.D.

GARGOYLES

IN THE MIDDLE AGES MANY CHURCHES AND CATHEDRALS IN
EUROPE WERE BUILT IN GOTHIC STYLE, WITH TALL SPIRES
AND A BIG ROUND WINDOW.
THE *GOTHIC ROSE*.

Mkill CC BY-SA 3.0,

TO PREVENT RAINWATER FROM
RUNNING DOWN THE WALLS, THEY
MADE WATER SPOUTS IN THE SHAPE
OF MONSTERS AND DRAGONS -
THE GARGOYLES. RAINWATER RAN OUT OF THEIR MOUTHS ONTO
THE STREET. THE NAME *GARGOYLE* COMES FROM THE LATIN
WORD *GARGULA* WHICH MEANS *THROAT*.
A LEGEND SAYS A FIRE-BREATHING DRAGON CALLED
LA GARGOUILLE WAS SINKING SHIPS ON THE
FRENCH RIVER SEINE. LOCAL PEOPLE SENT ONE
PERSON A YEAR TO BE EATEN BY THE DRAGON TO
KEEP IT FROM DESTROYING THEIR TOWN.
A CHRISTIAN PRIEST WHOSE NAME
WAS ROMANUS PROMISED THEM THAT IF THEY
WOULD BUILD A CHURCH, HE WOULD KILL THE
DRAGON. AND HE DID. THE HEAD OF THAT
DRAGON BECAME THE FIRST GARGOYLE.

The Tree Dragon Spell is really useful if there are large scary trees near your house. Maybe you noticed something strange in how their branches sway in the wind, or heard the creaky sounds they make at night?

Grownups keep telling you it's just the wind. Well, perhaps... but **you don't want to be a dragon's dinner if the grownups are wrong, do you?** This spell will help.

This spell is **a curse**. A curse is magic words calling for punishment or harm. Curses are only allowed in protection magic, and only when you are defending yourself from magical forces. If you put a curse on a human being, it's a crime.

To prepare the **Winter Curse Elixir**, find some dry plants - grass or leaves.

Step 1 - Separation:
Soak them for half a day in filtered rainwater.

Step 2 - Purification:
Get them out, wash them 3 times, and tear them into pieces (no metal knife or scissors!) Take the water in which you soaked these plants, and filter that water.

Step 3 - Recombination: Put the
pieces of leaves back into filtered water, and add a teaspoonful of salt. Mix well. Now go ahead and say the spell.

Dragon Spell 4 (2)

DRAGON'S THRONE, ROOTS OF STONE,
AT LIGHT OF DAWN
WITH THIS SPELL BE GONE.

1.

2.

3.

The Tree Dragon Spell

Mix some bark or leaves from
the dragon-haunted tree into
Winter Curse Elixir. Cast this
spell, and pour all the elixir
under the tree to the last drop.

Dragon's throne,
Roots of stone,
At light of dawn
With this curse, be gone.

YGGDRASIL

In ancient times people
of Northern Europe noticed that
dragons were attracted
to tall trees.
Legends of the Viking Age
(8-12 centuries A.D.) talk about
a giant ash tree called Yggdrasil
as the center of the universe.
The three roots of Yggdrasil drink
waters of the three worlds:
Asgard - the world of gods,
Midgard - the world of people, and
Helheim - the world of the dead.

At the bottom of the tree
lay a great dragon,
Nidhogg. Nidhogg eats
the roots of Yggdrasil.
Vikings believed that
the dragon was also
snacking on people
who broke a promise.

In the Viking world
not keeping your word
was a crime
as bad as a murder.

VIKING SHIPS AND HELMETS

VIKINGS FROM ANCIENT SCANDINAVIA IN NORTHERN
EUROPE WERE VERY GOOD AT
SEA TRAVEL. THEIR SHIPS
REACHED AMERICA LONG
BEFORE COLUMBUS.

ON THE BOW (FRONT TIP)
OF THEIR SHIPS VIKINGS
ALWAYS HAD THE HEAD OF A DRAGON
CARVED FROM WOOD TO SCARE OFF
SEA MONSTERS. WHENEVER THE SHIP CAME
CLOSE TO THE SHORE, THEY WOULD REMOVE
THE DRAGON HEAD FROM THE BOW SO AS
NOT TO SCARE ANYONE ON LAND!
WOW, SO NICE OF THEM.

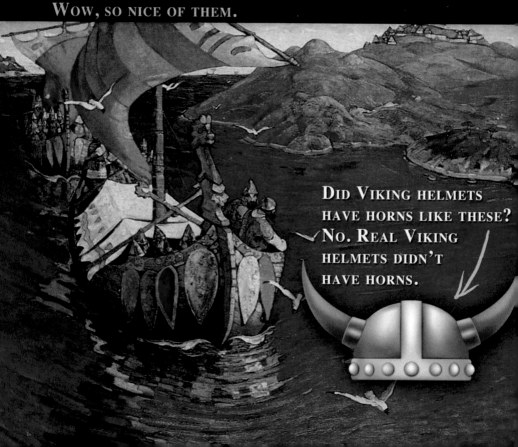

DID VIKING HELMETS
HAVE HORNS LIKE THESE?
NO. REAL VIKING
HELMETS DIDN'T
HAVE HORNS.

Dragon Spell 5

This page was floating on black waves at the top of the stairs leading to the flooded lower vaults of the North Landing library. There was an old photograph stuck to it. The words written on the photo say: *Focus and win* - in the same handwriting as one other page from the Dragon Spells book!

I went through a lot of documents at the North Landing library looking for clues about the girl in the photo. Her mom was a librarian, and it looks like the girl copied for herself some spells from ancient books that later perished in the floods. She must have been very skilled at magic.

Dragon in Your Mind is a simple spell, no potion. Cast it when you know something is wrong, and it's not because of you. Maybe you feel sad without any serious reason, or feel frustrated or tired when you should be full of energy... Maybe you feel angry and that anger is going to get you in trouble... It's possible that there is a dragon somewhere near, messing with you and tryng to trick you into doing something wrong.

That's when you strike it with this spell. I cast it many times when I was a kid, and it worked.

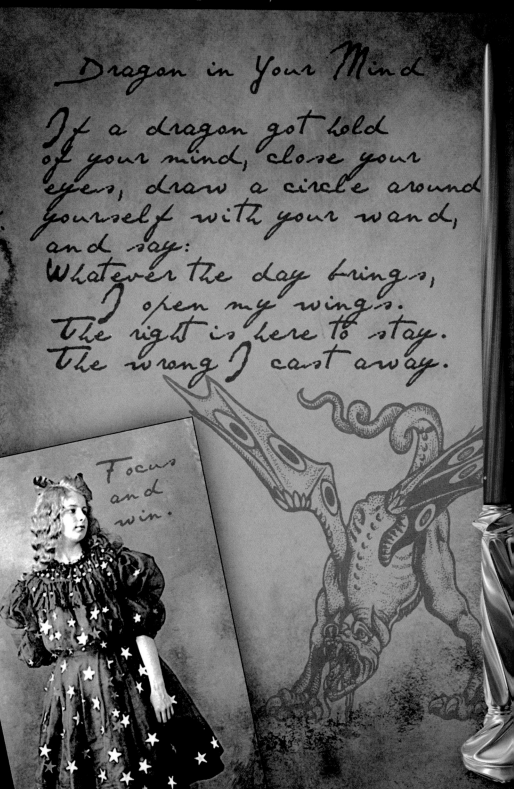

Dragon in Your Mind

If a dragon got hold
of your mind, close your
eyes, draw a circle around
yourself with your wand,
and say:
Whatever the day brings,
  I open my wings.
The right is here to stay.
The wrong I cast away.

Focus
and
win.

History of Alchemy (1)

In Ancient Egypt they didn't have scientists or alchemists. All the scientific discoveries and alchemy experiments were made by priests in the temples of Egyptian gods. They needed that knowledge to build more temples and tombs, to make mummies, to understand the laws of nature, and to convince the Egyptian kings, Pharaohs, that they got that knowledge from the gods (which, of course, wasn't true!) The priests had to promise to keep secret everything they learned - or die, so there is very little information about their alchemical work.

Pyramids and temple in Egypt

Then the Greek King Alexander the Great conquered Egypt around 300 B.C., and Greek scientists learned some secrets of Egyptian priests. Greeks called Egypt *Khem* or *Khemet*, which means *the Black Land*. Every year, in spring, the river Nile that flows from the South to the North of Egypt floods the fields around it, and washes a lot of black river dirt onto the fields. That's where the name *Black Land* came from. The scientists of ancient Greece and Rome called the secrets of Egyptian science and magic *Khemia The Black Art* - this is where our word chemistry comes from.

History of Alchemy (2)

The word *Alchemy* is *Khemia* plus the Arabic word *Al* (same as *The* in English) - *Al Khemia*. It's the same *Al* that we find in the word *Al Iksir* or *elixir* - an Arabic word for the mysterious potion that alchemists believed could turn any metal into gold.

In 290 A.D. Roman Emperor Diocletian ordered that all the alchemical books be destroyed, because he was afraid that alchemists would learn to make gold and become richer than the Emperor. Many alchemists moved away to the east, to Arab lands and Persia.

Diocletian
Photo: Zaza
SRB CC BY-SA

That's where *Khemia* became *Al Khemia* or *Alchemy*. Alchemy came back to Europe with the Islamic invasions that began around 800 A.D., when rulers of Arab lands tried to get Europeans to give up their Christian faith and switch to Islam.

The English word *gibberish* comes from the name of *Jabir ibn Hayaan*. Jabir was an Arab alchemist of that era, whose books were full of mysterious words and stories created to hide alchemical secrets.

Aljafería fortress in Aragon, Spain, built during the Islamic occupation of Spain

Photo by Ecelan

THE PHILOSOPHER'S STONE

AS WE KNOW, ONE OF THE GOALS OF ALCHEMY WAS TO INVENT THE PHILOSOPHER'S STONE THAT COULD TURN ANY METAL INTO GOLD. *LAPIS PHILOSOPHORUM* IN LATIN = *STONE OF THE PHILOSOPHERS*. THEY ALSO CALLED IT THE *ELIXIR OF LIFE* HOPING IT WOULD MAKE PEOPLE IMMORTAL.

IN THE 15TH OR 16TH CENTURIES, AN ALCHEMIST KNOWN UNDER THE NAME OF *BASILIUS VALENTINUS*, MADE 12 DRAWINGS THEY CALL THE 12 KEYS - THESE WERE THE STEPS TO MAKING THE PHILOSOPHER'S STONE. UNFORTUNATELY NOBODY COULD UNDERSTAND THE 12 KEYS. ONLY A FEW KEYS HAVE BEEN EXPLAINED. BELOW IS KEY 3 (*CLAVIS* = KEY IN LATIN).

IN THIS DRAWING, GOLD IS A ROOSTER, BECAUSE GOLD IS YELLOW AND SHINY LIKE THE SUN, AND ROOSTERS CROW WHEN THE SUN RISES. THE GOLD IS DISSOLVED (BECOMES LIQUID) IN ACID (A SUBSTANCE THAT CAN DESTROY OTHER SUBSTANCES). IN THE PICTURE, THE ACID IS A FOX WHO EATS THE ROOSTER. THEN GOLD IS HEATED AND TURNS INTO VAPOR (A DRAGON IN THE PICTURE), AND THEN THE VAPOR TURNS INTO RED CRYSTALS - THE ROOSTER EATING THE FOX!

Isaac Newton

The famous English scientist Isaac Newton was also an alchemist. The alchemical method of Separation, Purification, and Recombinaton helped him make a huge discovery in Optics (the science of light). He split white light into rainbow colors, and showed that white light is a mix of 7 colors - red, orange, yellow, green, blue, indigo, and violet. White light splits when it passes through an object that bends light. Red light doesn't bend easily, so in a rainbow it shows on top. Violet light bends the most, so it's always at the bottom of the rainbow. To bend light Newton used a prism, or a crystal with triangular base. When he saw the rainbow colors, he called them a *spectrum*, which means *ghost* in Latin.

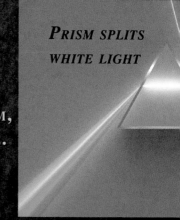

Prism splits white light

We still call the rainbow colors *the color spectrum*. For our next spell we need that ghost of a rainbow! As Newton did, you can use a crystal (like a chandelier crystal), or a crystal wine glass, or any transparent object that has sharp facets, or angles. But just in case you don't have any of these objects, on the next page I will teach you how to split white light using everyday things, like a drinking glass, or a mirror.

Make Your Own Rainbow

METHOD 1 - YOU CAN USE SUNLIGHT, OR A FLASH LIGHT.

CUT A NARROW WINDOW IN A PAPER RECTANGLE, AND TAPE IT TO A GLASS FULL OF WATER. MAKE SURE THE LIGHT SHINES THROUGH THIS WINDOW ONTO THE SURFACE OF THE WATER. TO MAKE THE RAINBOW BRIGHTER, I HOLD A SHEET OF PAPER BEHIND THE GLASS.

METHOD 2

PUT A SMALL MIRROR INTO A BOWL OF WATER, SO THAT HALF OF THE MIRROR IS UNDER WATER. LET THE LIGHT SHINE ONTO THE MIRROR, AND HOLD A SHEET OF PAPER OVER THE BOWL TO CATCH THE RAINBOW.

Mineral Alchemy

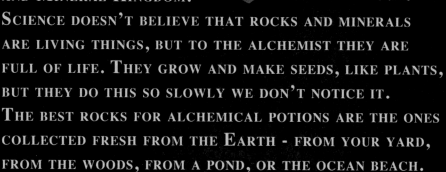

Alchemy divides the world into the
Plant Kingdom,
Animal Kingdom,
and Mineral Kingdom.
Science doesn't believe that rocks and minerals
are living things, but to the alchemist they are
full of life. They grow and make seeds, like plants,
but they do this so slowly we don't notice it.
The best rocks for alchemical potions are the ones
collected fresh from the Earth - from your yard,
from the woods, from a pond, or the ocean beach.

To cast the Rainbow Rock spell, find a small stone.
Add a teaspoonful of salt to half a cup of water,
drop the stone into the cup and swirl the water with
the spoon until all the salt is dissolved.
Now put the stone in a sunny spot
for an hour or more so
it absorbs the Sun's
energy,
the Solar Fire.

Next, make a rainbow,
and position the stone so
that the rainbow touches it.
Once the spell is cast,
put the stone near the
door outside your house.
Then take the water you used,
and toss it onto the ground
with your eyes closed.

The Rainbow Rock Spell

Select a stone to be
the Guardian of your door.

Let it drink of the rainbow,
and as it fills with the
invincible light, say:

No force, no will
Can break the rainbow door.
Dark shadow, melt!
Evil power is no more.

Hide the stone by your door.
It will shoot a rainbow beam
to stop any dragon, any
         ghost, any evil
            from entering
               your house.

Alchemical Fire

Fire in Alchemy is not the same as the flame of a candle. It is the **LIFE FORCE** of the world. For our next spell we'll prepare salt crystals rich in alchemical fire.

Spread the salt in a thin layer on a plate. Set the plate outside, protected from rain and dust, and keep it there overnight.

The salt will absorb water vapors always present in the air. These vapors carry the invisible *Universal Fire*, one of the *Alchemical Secret Fires*. Another one is the *Life Fire*, the energy coming from far away in the cosmos. On Earth it is carried by the air.

Now that the salt is rich with this special energy, put the plate in the sun and let it dry. If the salt melted and dissolved in water it absorbed from the air, drying will turn it into crystals again.

Alchemists talk about the *Sun behind the Sun*, or the source of spiritual energy that flows through the universe. They try to capture this energy, the *Solar Fire*, to extract it from the rays of the Sun. After the salt absorbs the sun energy and turns into crystals again, the life force locked inside these salt crystals is very pure and powerful.

Sand Potion

THE SAND POTION BUILDS AN
INVISIBLE SHIELD IN THE CLOUDS
OVER YOU, SO THE DRAGONS CAN'T SEE YOU.

COLLECT A CUP OF SAND FROM ANYWHERE - FROM THE YARD,
FROM A PLAYGROUND, OR FROM THE BEACH. WASH THE SAND
TO MAKE IT PURE. POUR IT INTO A JAR OF WATER
AND SHAKE WELL. THE SAND WILL FALL TO
THE BOTTOM OF THE JAR, BECAUSE IT IS
HEAVIER THAN WATER. BUT ANY BITS OF
DIRT AND PLANTS WILL FLOAT ON TOP,
BECAUSE THEY ARE LIGHTER THAN WATER.
POUR OUT THE DIRTY WATER. REPEAT THIS
A FEW TIMES, UNTIL THE SAND IS CLEAN.

SPREAD THE SAND IN A THIN LAYER AND
DRY IT IN THE SUN. NEXT, FOLD THE SAND
IN PAPER, OR IN A LARGE NAPKIN, PUT IT
ON THE PAVEMENT OR STONE OUTSIDE
AND STRIKE IT A FEW TIMES WITH A
HAMMER TO BREAK SOME SAND GRAINS
AND RELEASE THE ENERGY OF THE SAND
MINERALS. NOW THE SAND IS READY FOR
OUR POTION.

PUT 2 TABLESPOONS OF THIS CLEAN SAND
INTO A JAR OF WATER.
MIX IN 1 TEASPOONFUL OF FIRE-RICH
ALCHEMICAL SALT. LET THIS POTION
SIT IN THE SUN FOR AN HOUR.

Stand facing the East.
Dip your wand in the Sand
Potion. Say these words:

Fire of Life,
light up the East.
Light up the West
for the fire feast.
Close the gates
of Heaven so high,
With this circle, hide
Earth from sky.

Now draw a circle on the
ground with your wand, and
pour the Sand Potion out
following that circle.
Your spell is cast.

WHAT IS SAND?

SAND IS EVERYWHERE - ON THE BEACHES, BY THE RIVERS, AND IN DESERTS. IT HAS DIFFERENT COLORS IN DIFFERENT PLACES. IT'S WHITE ON THE BEACHES OF TROPICAL ISLANDS, AND IT'S BLACK ON THE BEACHES OF ICELAND. MOST SAND IS YELLOW, BECAUSE IT'S MADE FROM A MINERAL CALLED QUARTZ. WHEREVER YOU LIVE, MOST ROCKS YOU FIND HAVE QUARTZ IN THEM.

OVER MILLIONS OF YEARS, WIND, RAIN, AND WAVES BREAK THESE ROCKS INTO TINY PIECES AND POLISH THEM INTO SMOOTH GRAINS OF SAND.

SHELL AND CORAL

AROUND TROPICAL ISLANDS THE SAND IS MADE FROM PIECES OF CORAL REEFS AND SHELLS. THAT'S WHY IT'S WHITE. FISH BITE OFF PIECES OF CORAL TO EAT TINY CORAL WORMS WHO LIVE INSIDE. THE FISH CHEW THE CORAL INTO TINY GRAINS AND SPIT IT OUT. A LOT OF THAT WHITE TROPICAL SAND IS WHAT'S LEFT FROM THE FISH'S DINNER! THE BLACK BEACHES OF ICELAND ARE GRAINS OF BLACK ROCK FROM THE LOCAL VOLCANOES.

THE WHITE SAND OF A CARIBBEAN SEA BEACH, AND THE BLACK SAND OF ICELAND

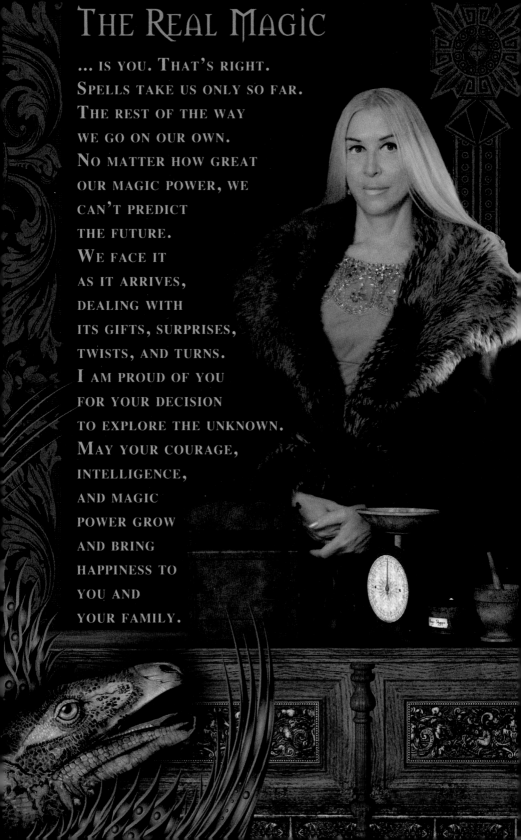

THE REAL MAGIC

... is you. That's right.
Spells take us only so far.
The rest of the way
we go on our own.
No matter how great
our magic power, we
can't predict
the future.
We face it
as it arrives,
dealing with
its gifts, surprises,
twists, and turns.
I am proud of you
for your decision
to explore the unknown.
May your courage,
intelligence,
and magic
power grow
and bring
happiness to
you and
your family.